All About Letters

Alphabet Puppets

by

Marilynn G. Barr

Aa
Aa

Publisher: Roberta Suid
Copy Editor: Carol Whiteley
Cover Design: David Hale

For a complete catalog, write to the address above.

Call our toll-free number: 1-800-255-6049
E-mail us at: MMBooks@aol.com
Visit our Web site:
http://www.mondaymorningbooks.com

monday
morning ®

ISBN 1-57612-139-9

Printed in the United States of America
9 8 7 6 5 4 3 2 1

Contents

Aa
Bb
Cc
Dd
Ee

Introduction

Introduce and reinforce alphabet recognition with the alphabet puppets in this book.

Puppets

Provide children with puppet patterns, crayons, scissors, glue, craft sticks, and tape. Demonstrate each step, as listed in the directions, while children assemble their puppets. Help children cut and attach Velcro squares to puppet hands and the backs of the picture cards for classroom or take-home alphabet practice puppets.

Alphabet Puppet Village (cover)

You will need seven soda cracker boxes, construction paper, scissors, glue, markers, and the alphabet puppet patterns (pages 5–56) to make this puppet village practice center. Cut off the tops and cover the boxes with construction paper. Cut out and glue rectangle doors, square windows, and triangle and circle attic windows to each box. Use a marker to draw details. Color, cut out, and assemble the alphabet puppets, excluding the storage pockets. Mount the puppets around the box houses. Cut and attach Velcro squares to puppet hands and the backs of picture cards. Store matching picture cards in the appropriate house. Set up your alphabet village in the centers area of your classroom. Encourage children to work in small groups to help each other identify and attach appropriate picture cards to the puppet with the matching beginning letter sound.

Show and Tell Alphabet

Make this a whole class activity or small group practice center. Decorate a sheet of poster board as shown. Attach several Velcro hat rack strips across the top. Color and cut out the show and tell patterns and cards (pages 57–64). Mount the puppets on the board. Cut and glue Velcro squares to each puppet as shown and to the backs of hats and picture cards. Attach a small paper bag between the puppets to store the picture cards. Mount the finished poster on your bulletin board or display it in your centers area. Invite children, in turn, to pick, identify, and attach a picture card to a puppet. Encourage each child to tell the class something about the picture. Then ask the student to pick out and attach the matching letter hat to the same puppet.

Aa
Bb
Aa
Velcro
Velcro
Show and Tell
Alphabet
Aa
Bb
Cc
Dd
Ee
Ff
Gg
Hh
Ss

My **Cc** Puppet

Materials

crayons or markers
scissors
glue
craft stick
tape

Directions

1. Color and cut out the patterns.
2. Glue the clothes to the puppet.
3. Glue a craft stick to the back of the puppet.
4. Tape the pocket to the back of the puppet.
5. Store the pictures in the pocket.

Cc
Back
Pocket
Cc

Puppet Clothes, Pocket, and Things That Start with Letter **Cc**

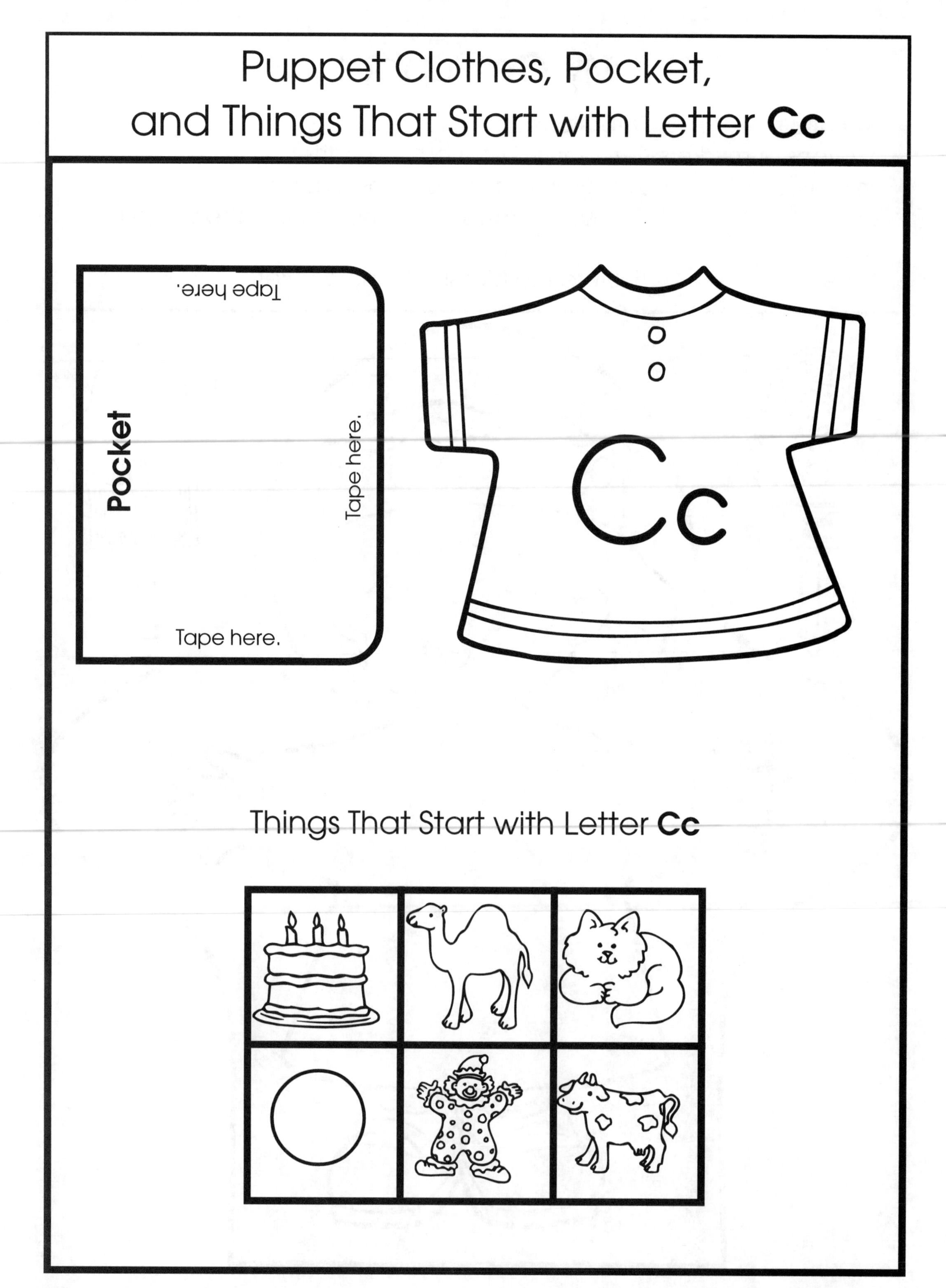

Tape here.
Pocket
Tape here.
Tape here.
Cc
Things That Start with Letter **Cc**

My **Dd** Puppet

Materials

crayons or markers
scissors
glue
craft stick
tape

Directions

1. Color and cut out the patterns.
2. Glue the clothes to the puppet.
3. Glue a craft stick to the back of the puppet.
4. Tape the pocket to the back of the puppet.
5. Store the pictures in the pocket.

Dd
Back
Pocket
Dd

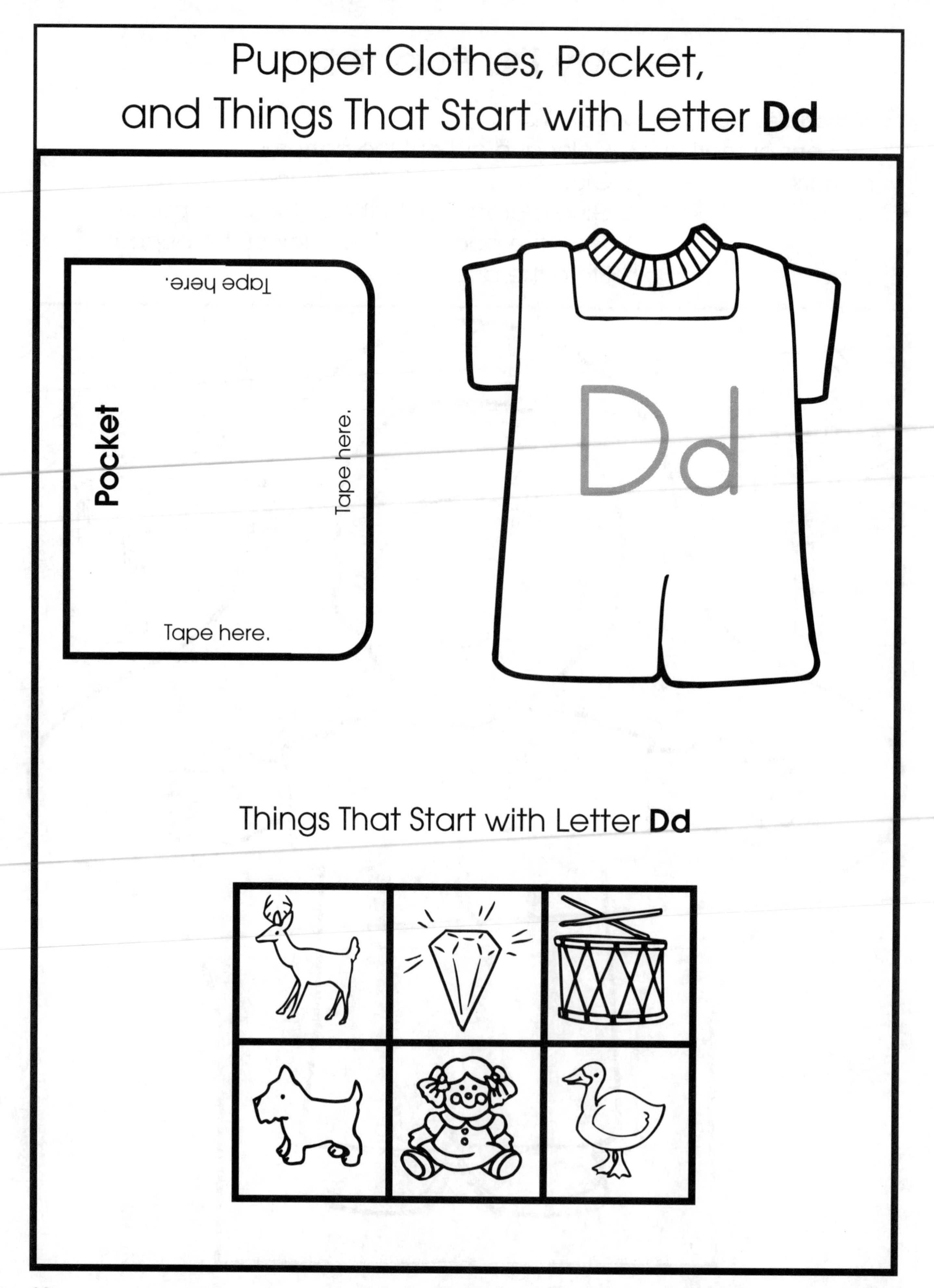
Puppet Clothes, Pocket,
and Things That Start with Letter Dd
Tape here.
Pocket
Tape here.
Tape here.
Dd
Things That Start with Letter Dd

My **Ee** Puppet

Materials
crayons or markers
scissors
glue
craft stick
tape

Directions
1. Color and cut out the patterns.
2. Glue the clothes to the puppet.
3. Glue a craft stick to the back of the puppet.
4. Tape the pocket to the back of the puppet.
5. Store the pictures in the pocket.

Ee

Back

Pocket

Ee

Puppet Clothes, Pocket, and Things That Start with Letter **Ee**

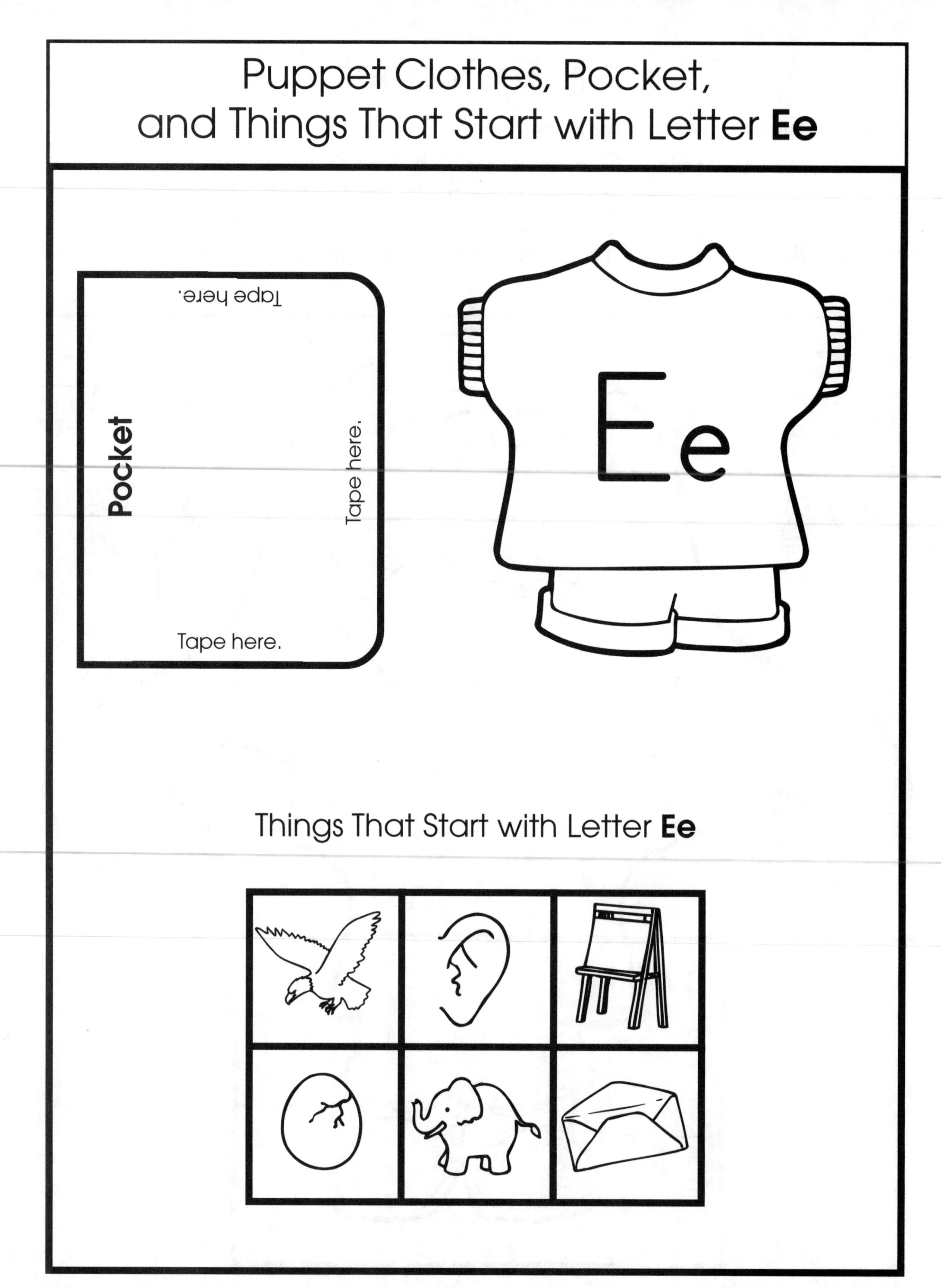
Tape here.
Pocket
Tape here.
Tape here.
Ee
Things That Start with Letter Ee

My **Ff** Puppet

Materials
crayons or markers
scissors
glue
craft stick
tape

Directions
1. Color and cut out the patterns.
2. Glue the clothes to the puppet.
3. Glue a craft stick to the back of the puppet.
4. Tape the pocket to the back of the puppet.
5. Store the pictures in the pocket.

Ff
Back
Pocket
Ff

Puppet Clothes, Pocket, and Things That Start with Letter **Ff**

Tape here.
Pocket
Tape here.
Tape here.
Ff

Things That Start with Letter **Ff**

My **Gg** Puppet

Materials

crayons or markers
scissors
glue
craft stick
tape

Directions

1. Color and cut out the patterns.
2. Glue the clothes to the puppet.
3. Glue a craft stick to the back of the puppet.
4. Tape the pocket to the back of the puppet.
5. Store the pictures in the pocket.

Gg
Back
Pocket
Gg

Puppet Clothes, Pocket, and Things That Start with Letter **Gg**

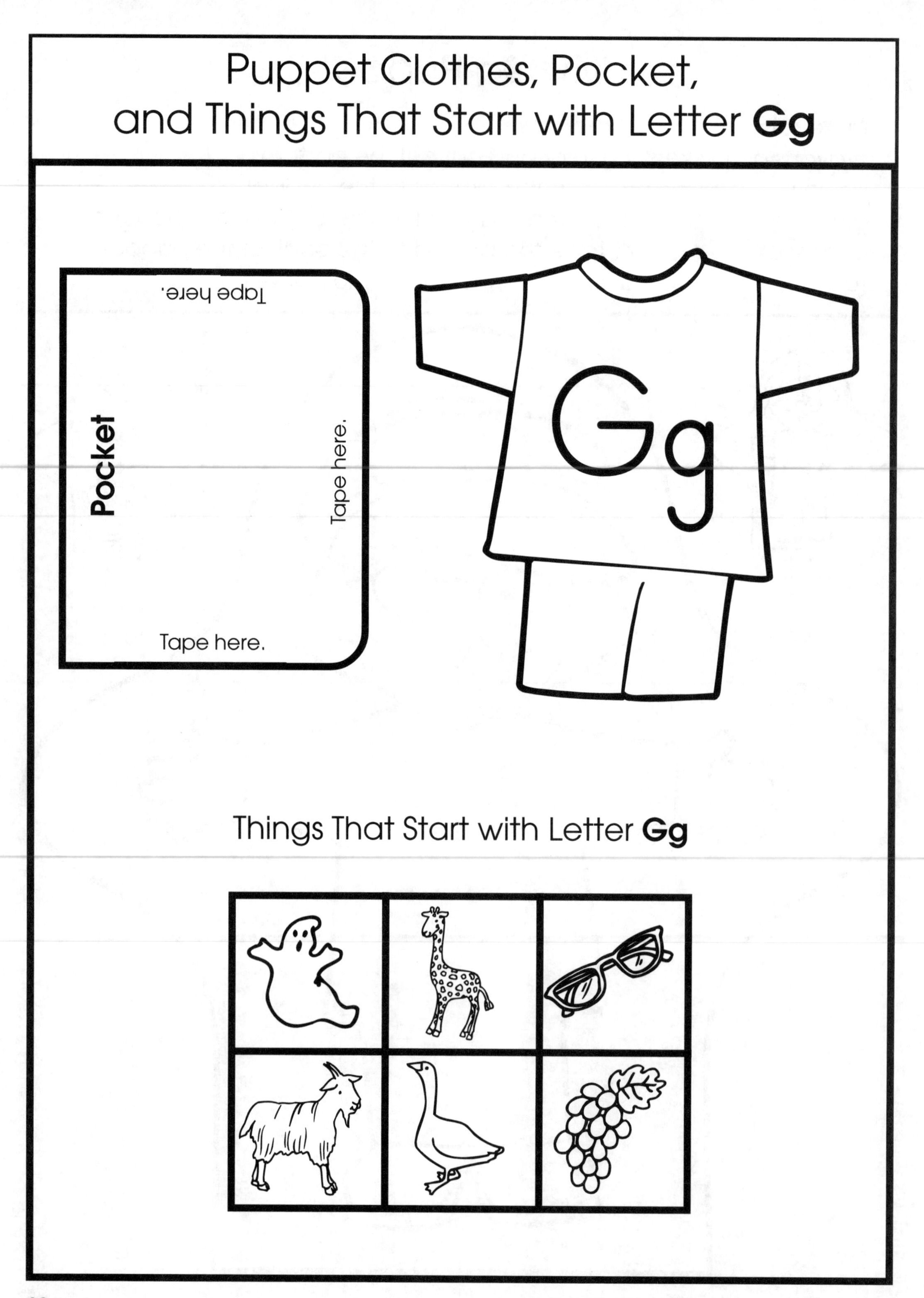
Tape here.
Pocket
Tape here.
Tape here.
Gg
Things That Start with Letter **Gg**

My **Hh** Puppet

Materials

crayons or markers
scissors
glue
craft stick
tape

Directions

1. Color and cut out the patterns.
2. Glue the clothes to the puppet.
3. Glue a craft stick to the back of the puppet.
4. Tape the pocket to the back of the puppet.
5. Store the pictures in the pocket.

Hh
Back
Pocket
Hh

Puppet Clothes, Pocket, and Things That Start with Letter **Hh**

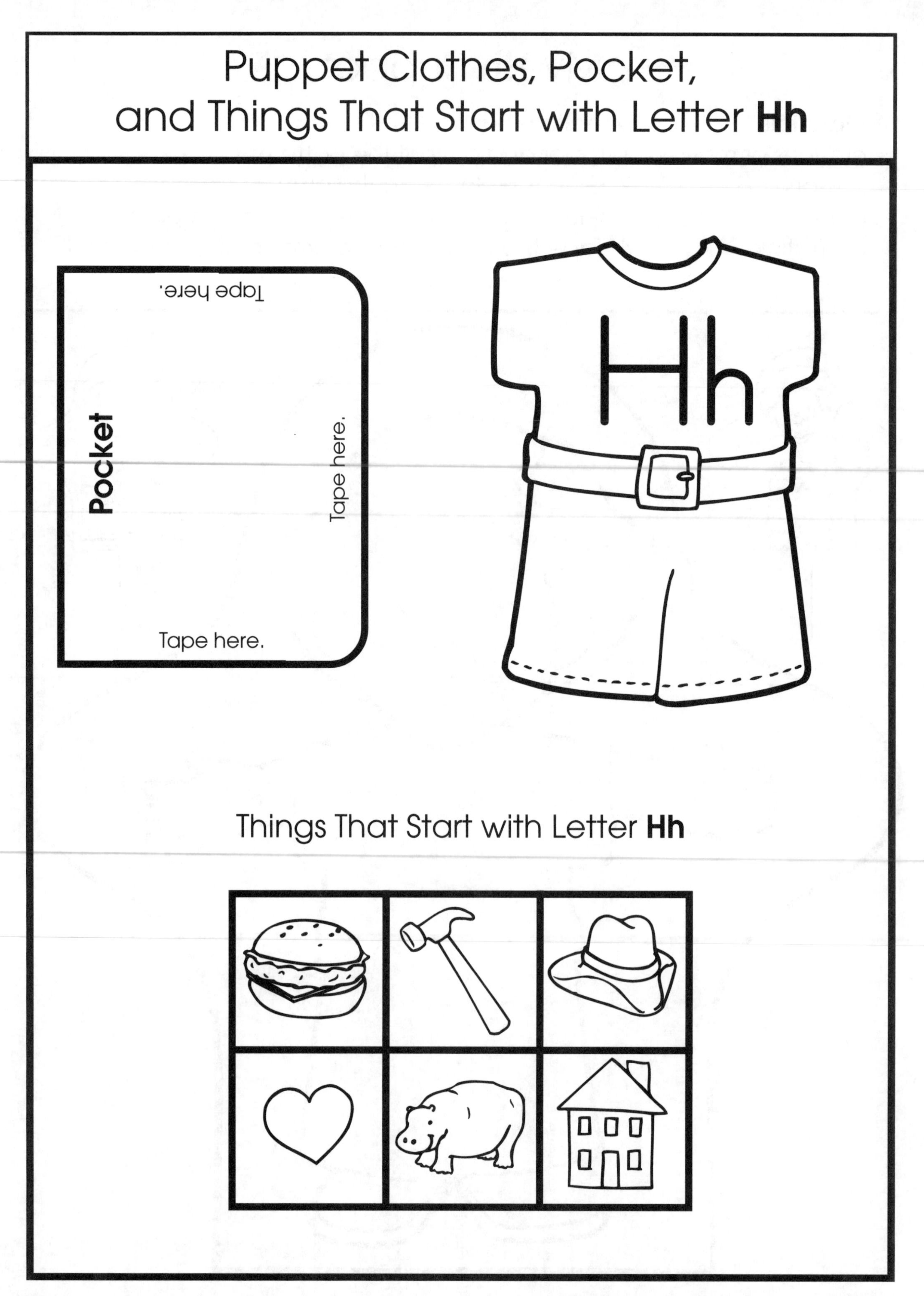

Tape here.
Pocket
Tape here.
Tape here.
Hh
Things That Start with Letter Hh

My **Ii** Puppet

Materials
crayons or markers
scissors
glue
craft stick
tape

Directions
1. Color and cut out the patterns.
2. Glue the clothes to the puppet.
3. Glue a craft stick to the back of the puppet.
4. Tape the pocket to the back of the puppet.
5. Store the pictures in the pocket.

Ii
Back
Pocket
Ii

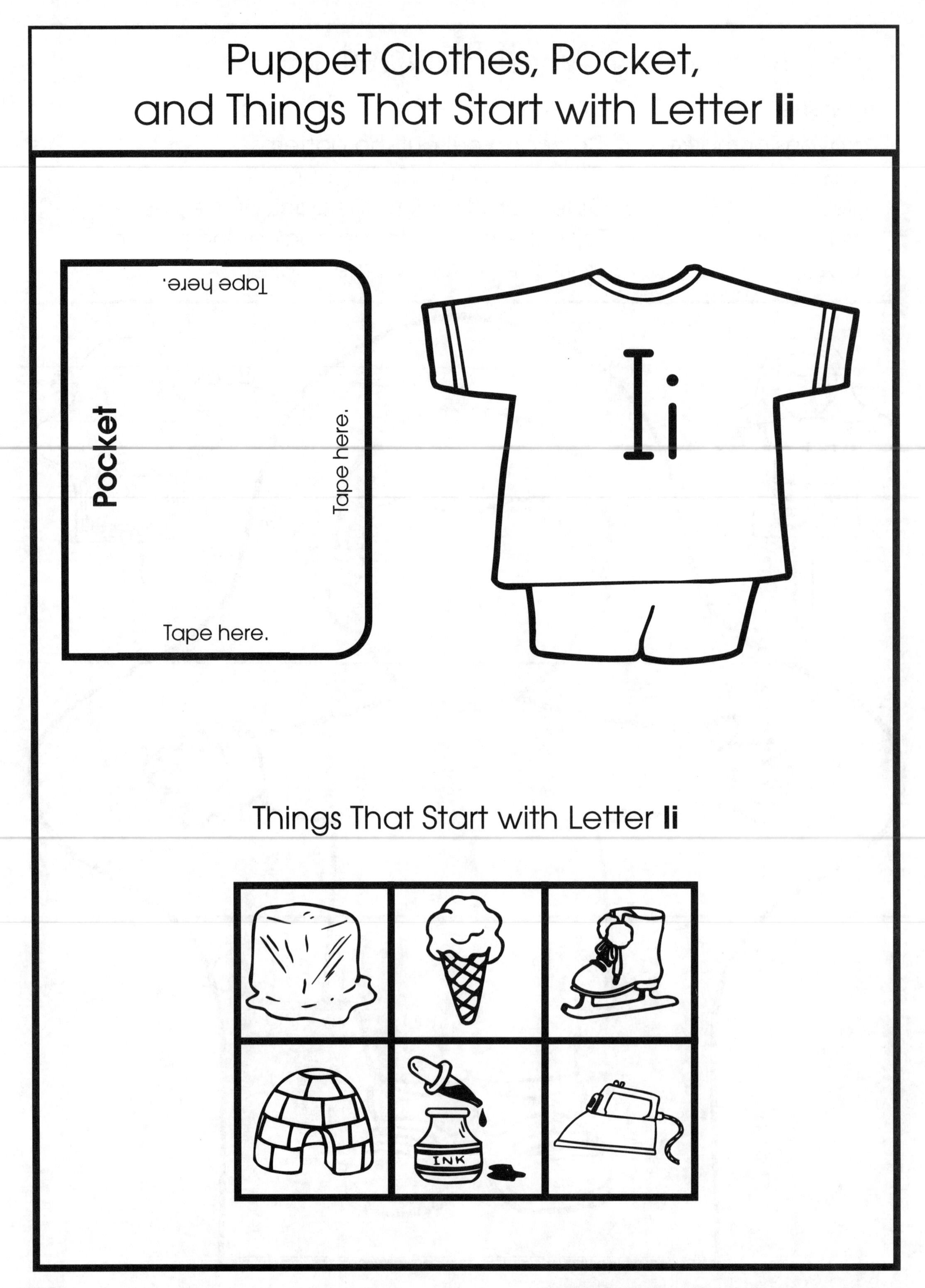
Puppet Clothes, Pocket,
and Things That Start with Letter **Ii**
Tape here.
Pocket
Tape here.
Tape here.
Ii
Things That Start with Letter **Ii**
INK

My **Jj** Puppet

Materials
crayons or markers
scissors
glue
craft stick
tape

Directions
1. Color and cut out the patterns.
2. Glue the clothes to the puppet.
3. Glue a craft stick to the back of the puppet.
4. Tape the pocket to the back of the puppet.
5. Store the pictures in the pocket.

Jj
Back
Pocket
Jj

Puppet Clothes, Pocket, and Things That Start with Letter **Jj**

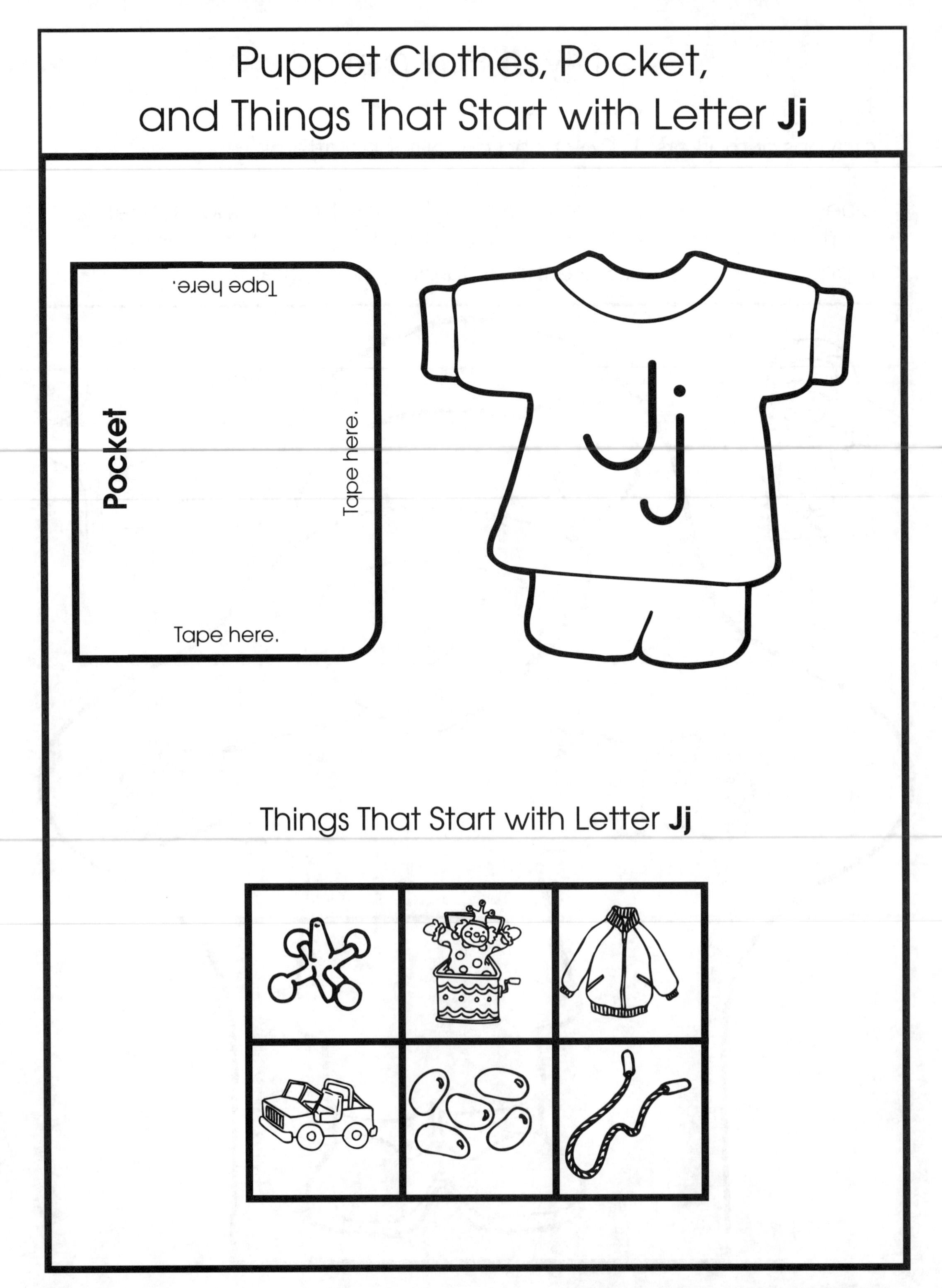
Tape here.
Pocket
Tape here.
Tape here.
Jj
Things That Start with Letter Jj

My **Kk** Puppet

Materials
crayons or markers
scissors
glue
craft stick
tape

Directions
1. Color and cut out the patterns.
2. Glue the clothes to the puppet.
3. Glue a craft stick to the back of the puppet.
4. Tape the pocket to the back of the puppet.
5. Store the pictures in the pocket.

Kk
Back
Pocket
Kk

Puppet Clothes, Pocket, and Things That Start with Letter **Kk**

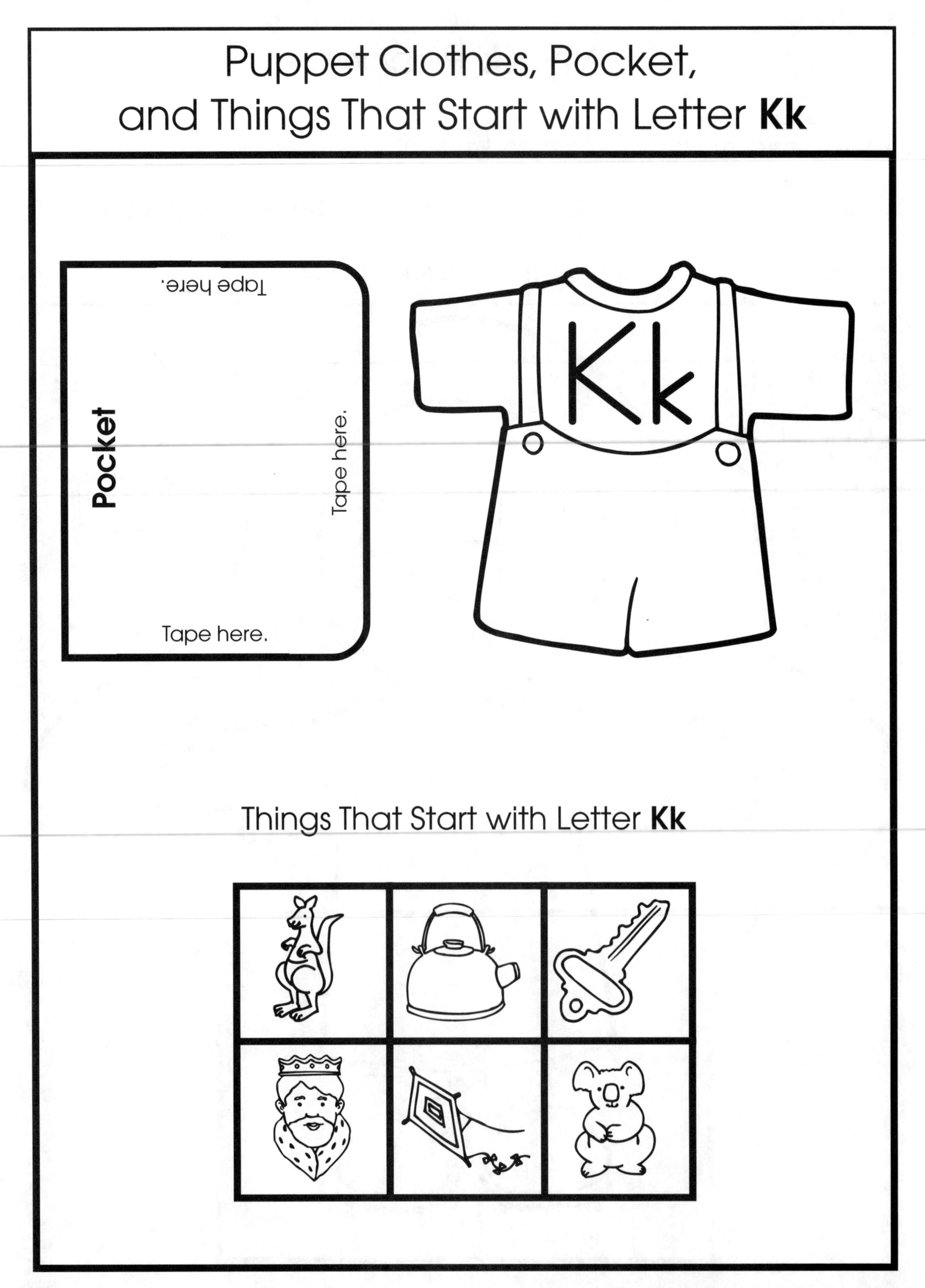
Tape here.
Pocket
Tape here.
Tape here.
Kk
Things That Start with Letter Kk

My **Ll** Puppet

Materials

crayons or markers
scissors
glue
craft stick
tape

Directions

1. Color and cut out the patterns.
2. Glue the clothes to the puppet.
3. Glue a craft stick to the back of the puppet.
4. Tape the pocket to the back of the puppet.
5. Store the pictures in the pocket.

Ll
Back
Pocket
Ll

Puppet Clothes, Pocket, and Things That Start with Letter **Ll**

Tape here.
Pocket
Tape here.
Tape here.
Ll
Things That Start with Letter Ll

My **Mm** Puppet

Materials

crayons or markers
scissors
glue
craft stick
tape

Directions

1. Color and cut out the patterns.
2. Glue the clothes to the puppet.
3. Glue a craft stick to the back of the puppet.
4. Tape the pocket to the back of the puppet.
5. Store the pictures in the pocket.

Mm
Back
Pocket
Mm

Puppet Clothes, Pocket, and Things That Start with Letter **Mm**

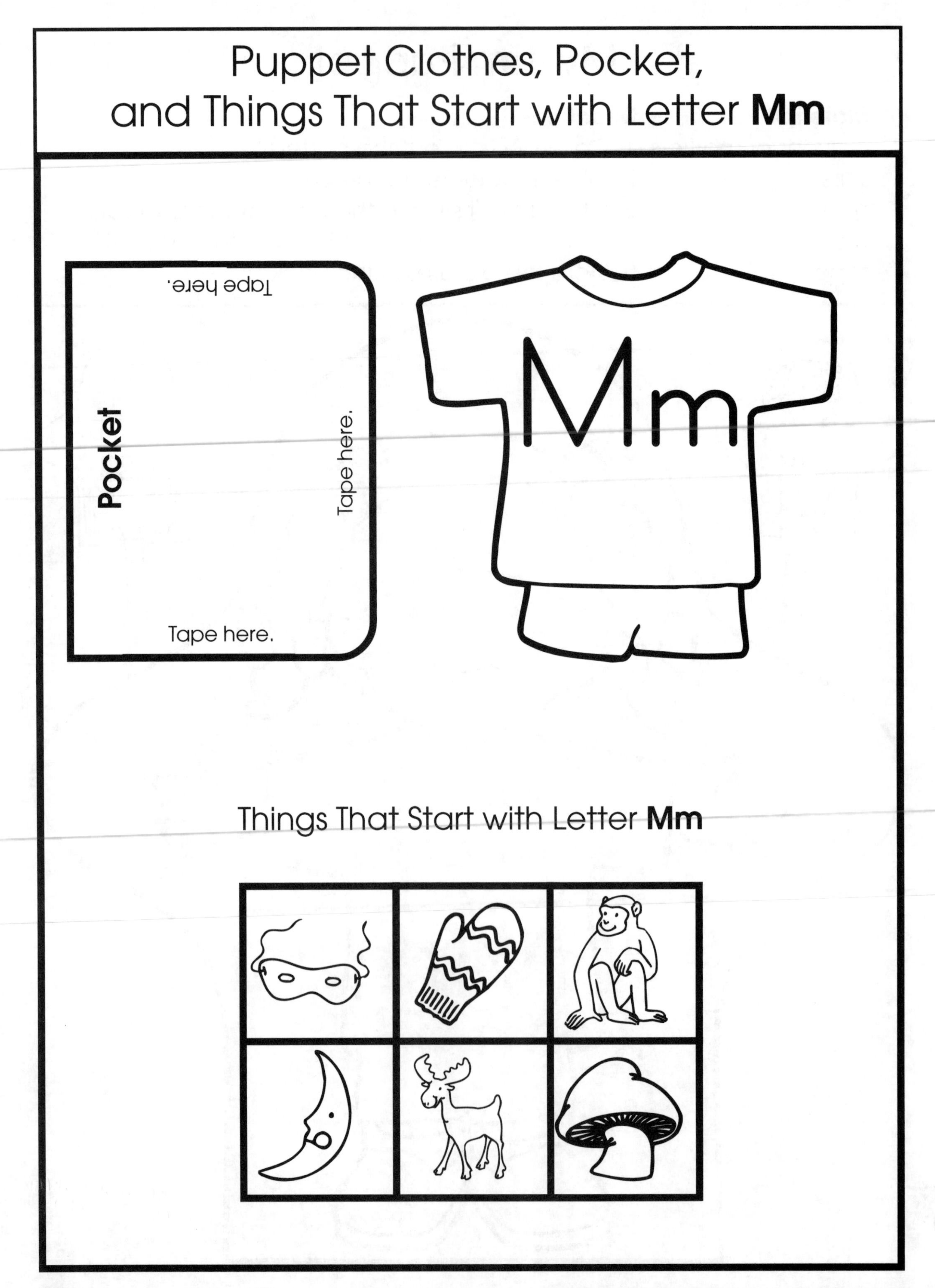
Tape here.
Pocket
Tape here.
Tape here.
Mm
Things That Start with Letter Mm

My **Nn** Puppet

Materials

crayons or markers
scissors
glue
craft stick
tape

Directions

1. Color and cut out the patterns.
2. Glue the clothes to the puppet.
3. Glue a craft stick to the back of the puppet.
4. Tape the pocket to the back of the puppet.
5. Store the pictures in the pocket.

Nn
Back
Pocket
Nn

Puppet Clothes, Pocket, and Things That Start with Letter Nn
Tape here.
Pocket
Tape here.
Tape here.
Nn
Things That Start with Letter Nn
NEWS

My **Oo** Puppet

Materials

crayons or markers
scissors
glue
craft stick
tape

Directions

1. Color and cut out the patterns.
2. Glue the clothes to the puppet.
3. Glue a craft stick to the back of the puppet.
4. Tape the pocket to the back of the puppet.
5. Store the pictures in the pocket.

Oo

Back

Pocket

Oo

Puppet Clothes, Pocket, and Things That Start with Letter **Oo**

Tape here.
Pocket
Tape here.
Tape here.
Oo
Things That Start with Letter **Oo**

My **Pp** Puppet

Materials

crayons or markers
scissors
glue
craft stick
tape

Directions

1. Color and cut out the patterns.
2. Glue the clothes to the puppet.
3. Glue a craft stick to the back of the puppet.
4. Tape the pocket to the back of the puppet.
5. Store the pictures in the pocket.

Pp
Back
Pocket
Pp

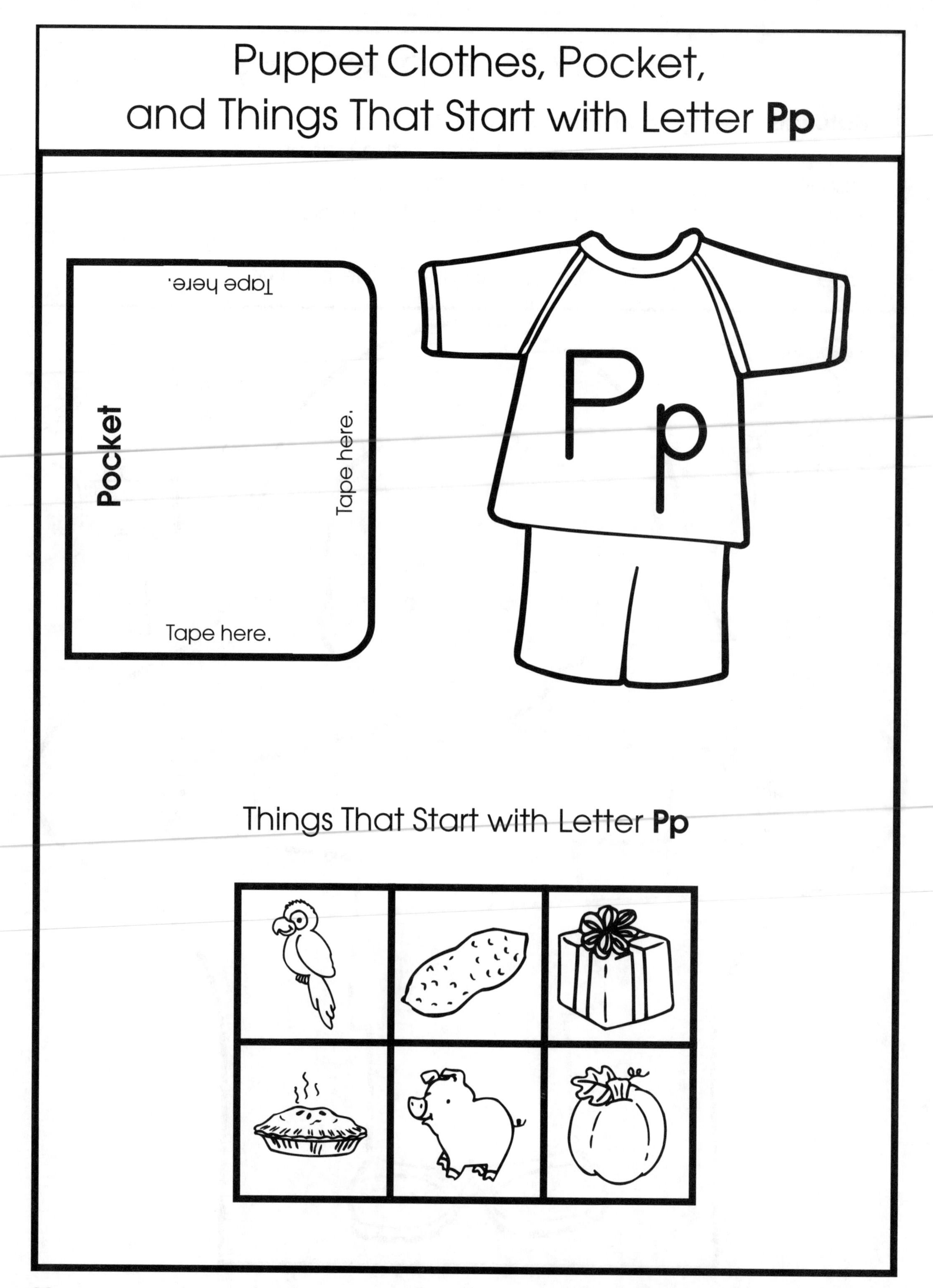
Puppet Clothes, Pocket,
and Things That Start with Letter **Pp**
Tape here.
Pocket
Tape here.
Tape here.
Pp
Things That Start with Letter **Pp**

My Qq Puppet

Materials
crayons or markers
scissors
glue
craft stick
tape

Directions
1. Color and cut out the patterns.
2. Glue the clothes to the puppet.
3. Glue a craft stick to the back of the puppet.
4. Tape the pocket to the back of the puppet.
5. Store the pictures in the pocket.

Qq
Back
Pocket
Qq

Puppet Clothes, Pocket, and Things That Start with Letter Qq

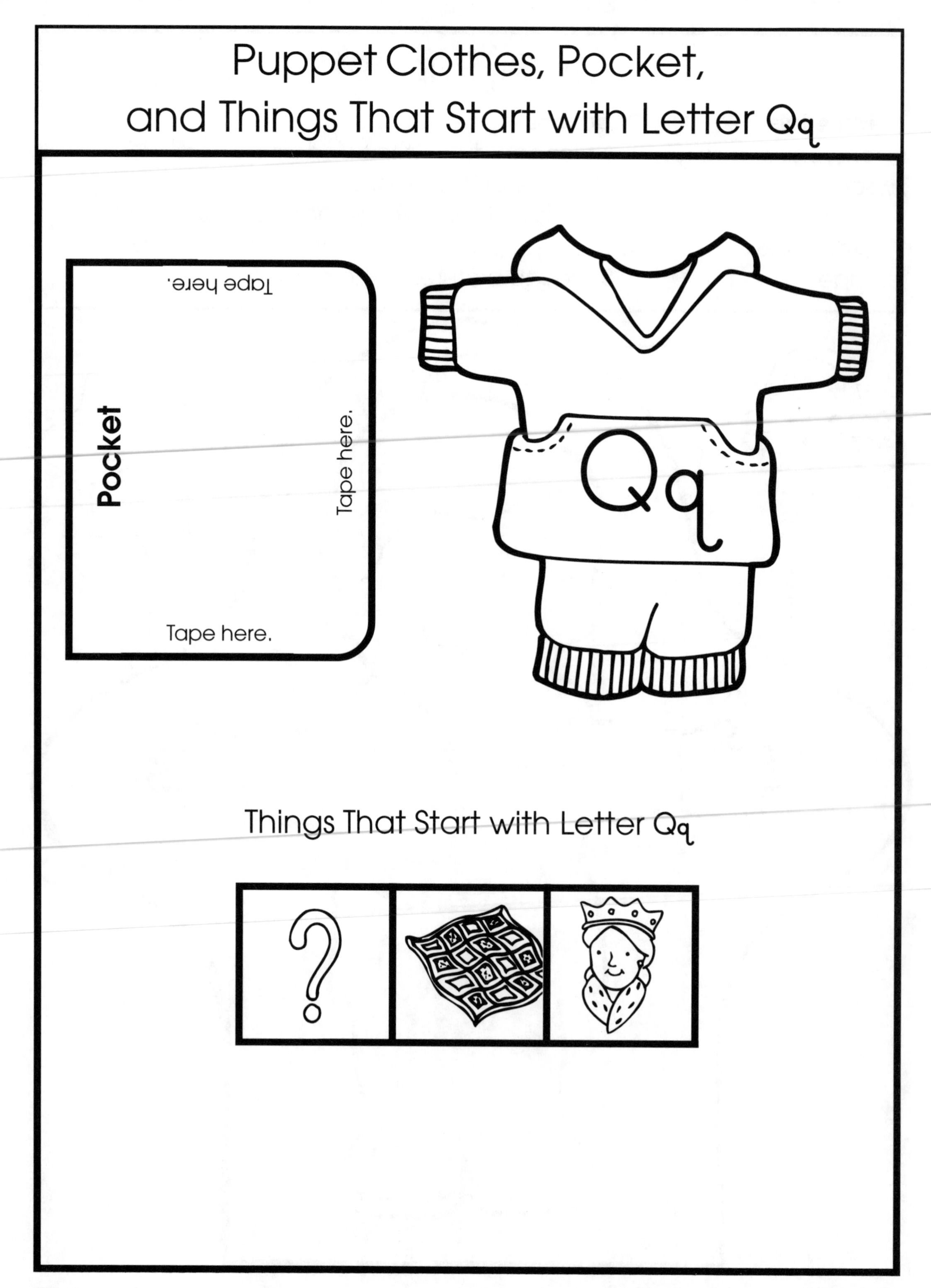
Tape here.
Pocket
Tape here.
Tape here.
Qq
Things That Start with Letter Qq

My **Rr** Puppet

Materials	**Directions**
crayons or markers	1. Color and cut out the patterns.
scissors	2. Glue the clothes to the puppet.
glue	3. Glue a craft stick to the back of the puppet.
craft stick	4. Tape the pocket to the back of the puppet.
tape	5. Store the pictures in the pocket.

Rr
Back
Pocket
Rr

Puppet Clothes, Pocket,
and Things That Start with Letter **Rr**
Tape here.
Pocket
Tape here.
Tape here.
Rr
Things That Start with Letter **Rr**

My **Ss** Puppet

Materials

crayons or markers
scissors
glue
craft stick
tape

Directions

1. Color and cut out the patterns.
2. Glue the clothes to the puppet.
3. Glue a craft stick to the back of the puppet.
4. Tape the pocket to the back of the puppet.
5. Store the pictures in the pocket.

Ss
Back
Pocket
Ss

Puppet Clothes, Pocket, and Things That Start with Letter **Ss**

Tape here.
Pocket
Tape here.
Tape here.
Ss
Things That Start with Letter Ss

My **Tt** Puppet

Materials

crayons or markers
scissors
glue
craft stick
tape

Directions

1. Color and cut out the patterns.
2. Glue the clothes to the puppet.
3. Glue a craft stick to the back of the puppet.
4. Tape the pocket to the back of the puppet.
5. Store the pictures in the pocket.

Tt
Back
Pocket
Tt

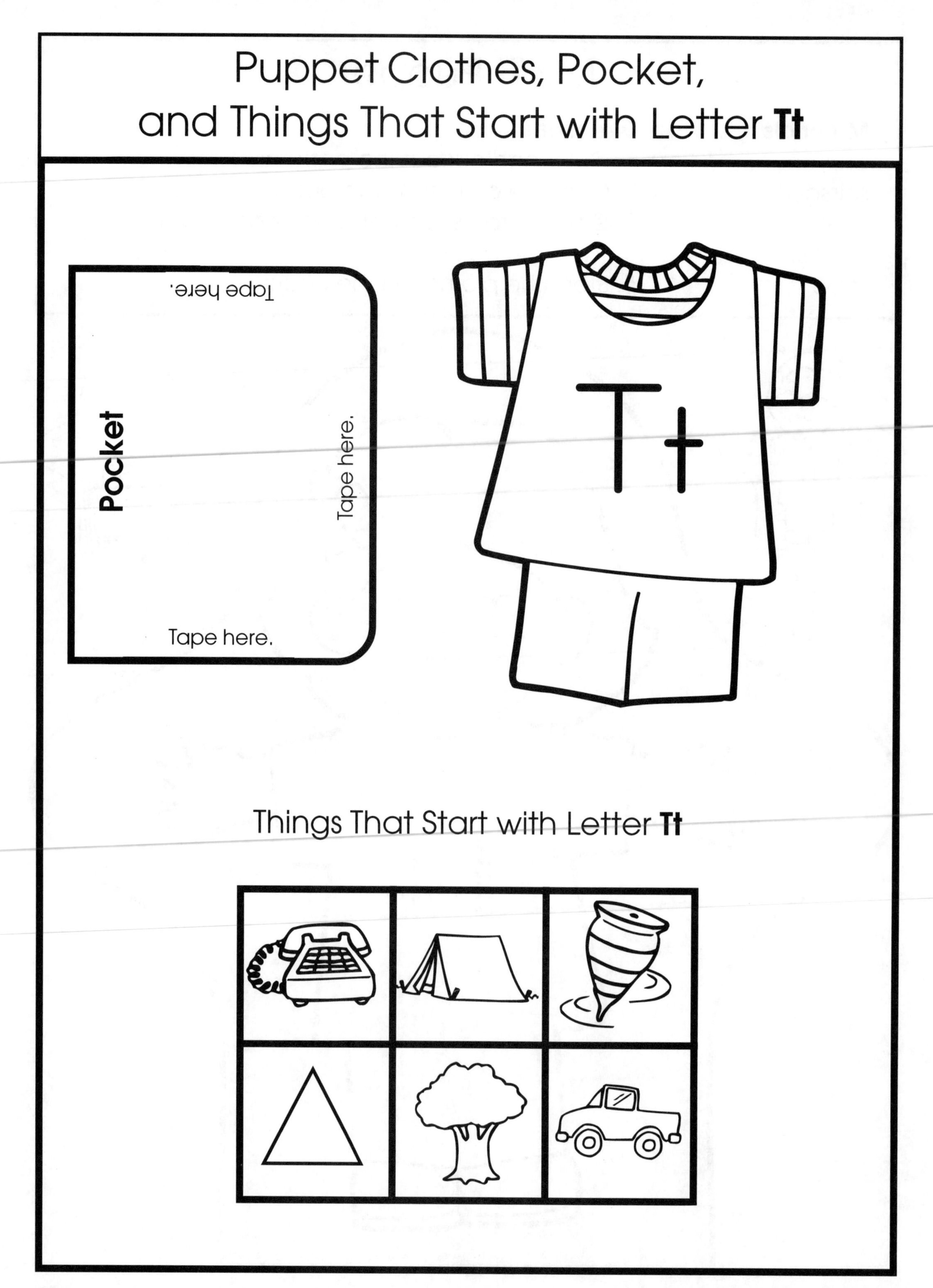
Puppet Clothes, Pocket,
and Things That Start with Letter Tt
Tape here.
Pocket
Tape here.
Tape here.
Tt
Things That Start with Letter Tt

My **Uu** Puppet

Materials
crayons or markers
scissors
glue
craft stick
tape

Directions
1. Color and cut out the patterns.
2. Glue the clothes to the puppet.
3. Glue a craft stick to the back of the puppet.
4. Tape the pocket to the back of the puppet.
5. Store the pictures in the pocket.

U u
Back
Pocket
Uu

Puppet Clothes, Pocket, and Things That Start with Letter **Uu**

Tape here.
Pocket
Tape here.
Tape here.
U u
Things That Start with Letter **Uu**

My **Vv** Puppet

Materials

crayons or markers
scissors
glue
craft stick
tape

Directions

1. Color and cut out the patterns.
2. Glue the clothes to the puppet.
3. Glue a craft stick to the back of the puppet.
4. Tape the pocket to the back of the puppet.
5. Store the pictures in the pocket.

Vv
Back
Pocket
Vv

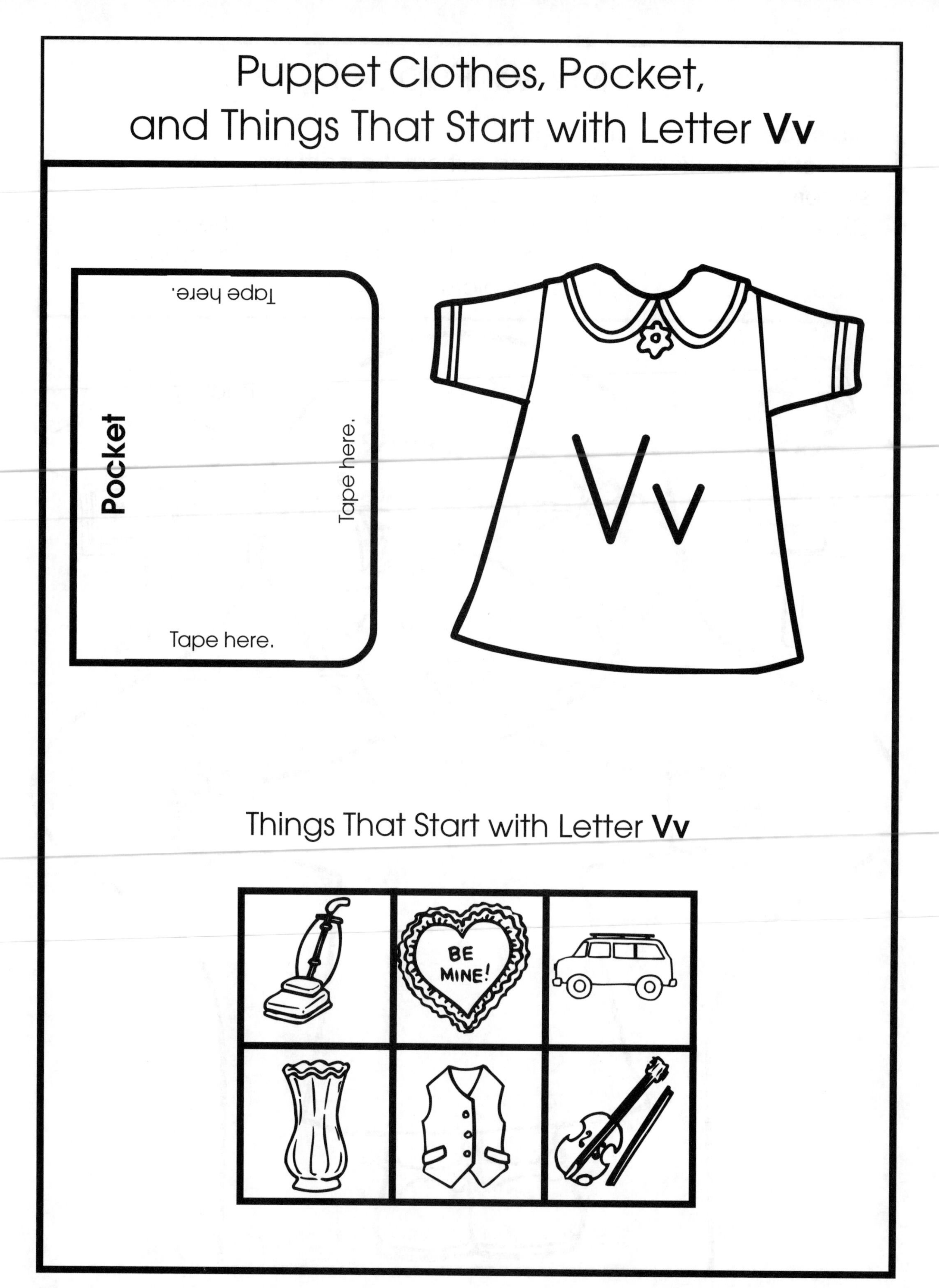
Puppet Clothes, Pocket,
and Things That Start with Letter Vv
Tape here.
Pocket
Tape here.
Tape here.
Vv
Things That Start with Letter Vv
BE
MINE!

My **Ww** Puppet

Materials

crayons or markers
scissors
glue
craft stick
tape

Directions

1. Color and cut out the patterns.
2. Glue the clothes to the puppet.
3. Glue a craft stick to the back of the puppet.
4. Tape the pocket to the back of the puppet.
5. Store the pictures in the pocket.

Ww
Back
Pocket
Ww

Puppet Clothes, Pocket, and Things That Start with Letter **Ww**

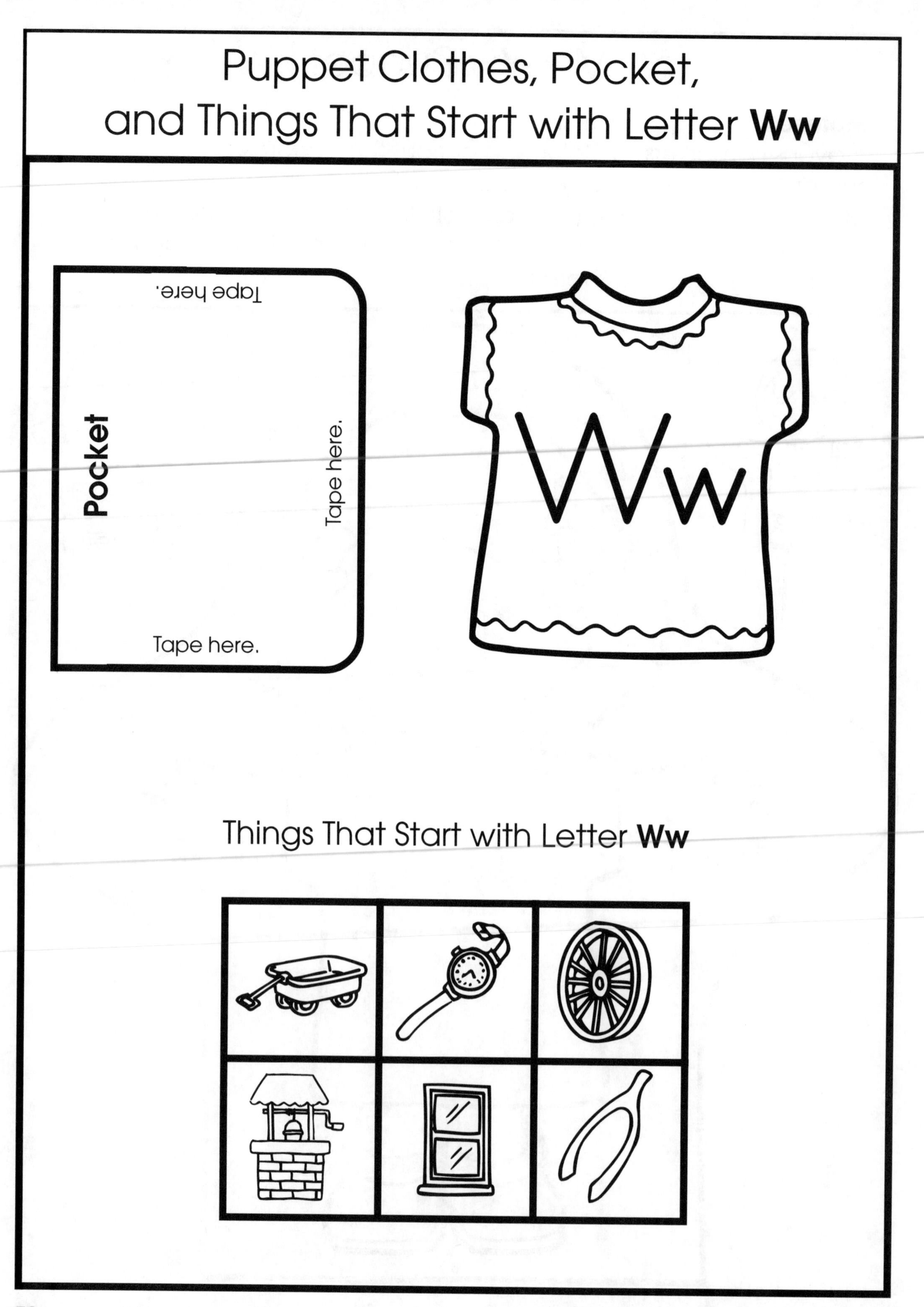

Tape here.
Pocket
Tape here.
Tape here.
Ww
Things That Start with Letter Ww

My **Xx** Puppet

Materials

crayons or markers
scissors
glue
craft stick
tape

Directions

1. Color and cut out the patterns.
2. Glue the clothes to the puppet.
3. Glue a craft stick to the back of the puppet.
4. Tape the pocket to the back of the puppet.
5. Store the pictures in the pocket.

Xx
Back
Pocket
Xx

Puppet Clothes, Pocket, and Things That Start with Letter **Xx**

Tape here.
Pocket
Tape here.
Tape here.
Xx

Things That Start with Letter **Xx**

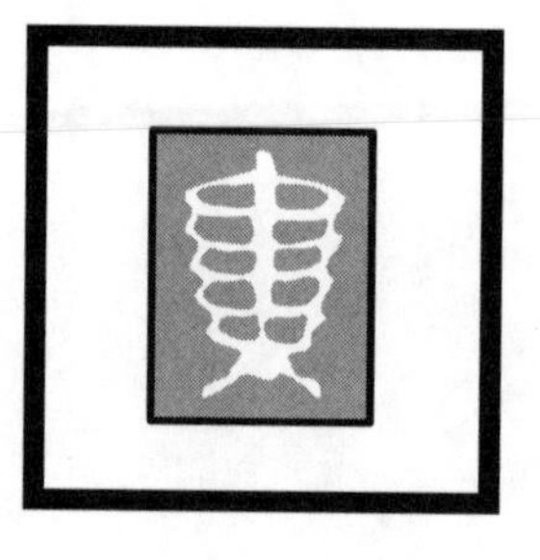

My **Yy** Puppet

Materials
crayons or markers
scissors
glue
craft stick
tape

Directions
1. Color and cut out the patterns.
2. Glue the clothes to the puppet.
3. Glue a craft stick to the back of the puppet.
4. Tape the pocket to the back of the puppet.
5. Store the pictures in the pocket.

Yy
Back
Pocket
Yy

Puppet Clothes, Pocket, and Things That Start with Letter **Yy**

Tape here.
Pocket
Tape here.
Tape here.
Yy
Things That Start with Letter **Yy**

My **Zz** Puppet

Materials

crayons or markers
scissors
glue
craft stick
tape

Directions

1. Color and cut out the patterns.
2. Glue the clothes to the puppet.
3. Glue a craft stick to the back of the puppet.
4. Tape the pocket to the back of the puppet.
5. Store the pictures in the pocket.

Zz
Back
Pocket
Zz

Puppet Clothes, Pocket, and Things That Start with Letter **Zz**

Tape here.
Pocket
Tape here.
Tape here.
Z z
Things That Start with Letter Zz

Show and Tell Patterns

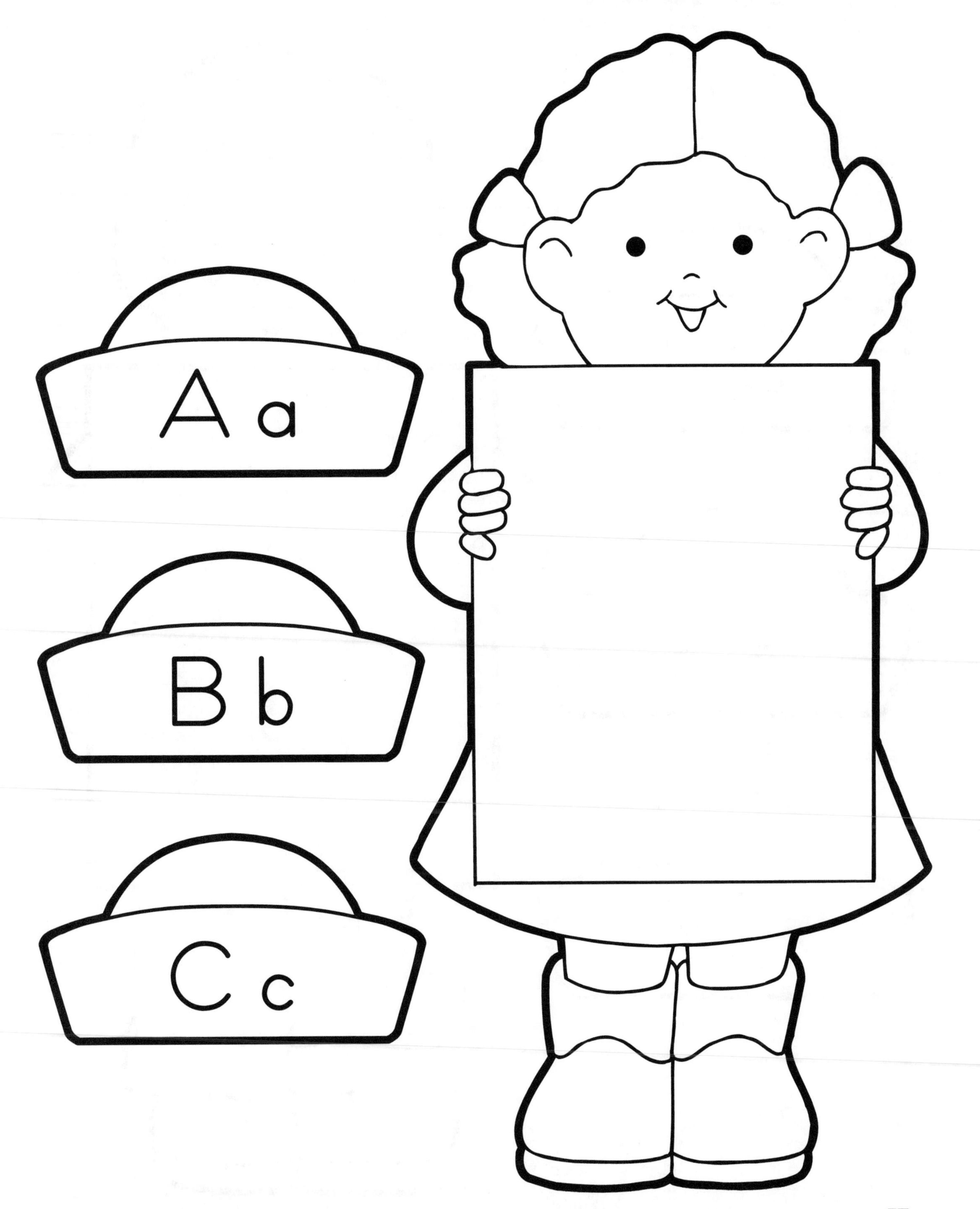
Aa
Bb
Cc

Show and Tell Patterns

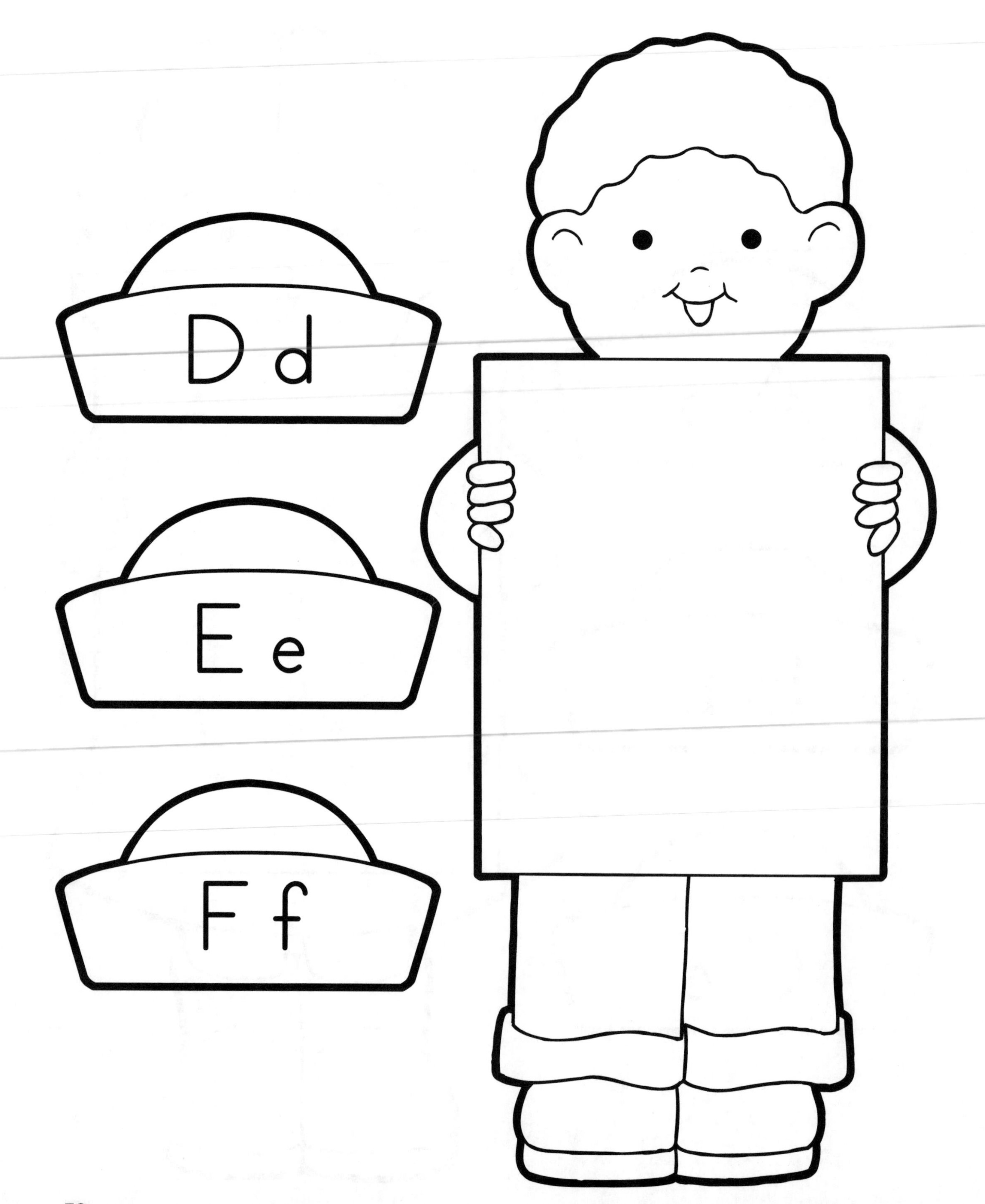

Dd
Ee
Ff

Show and Tell Patterns

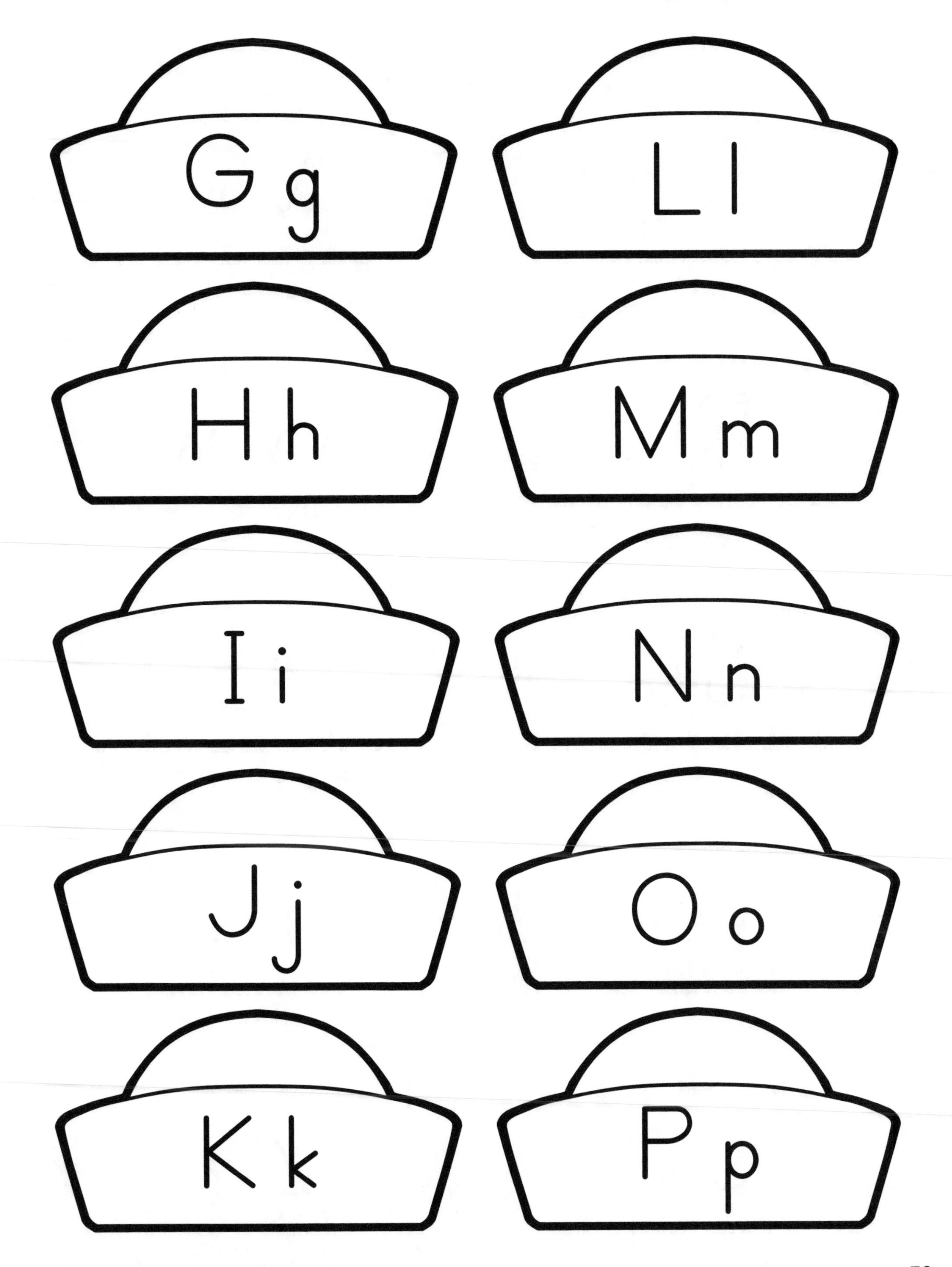

Gg
Ll
Hh
Mm
Ii
Nn
Jj
Oo
Kk
Pp

Show and Tell Patterns

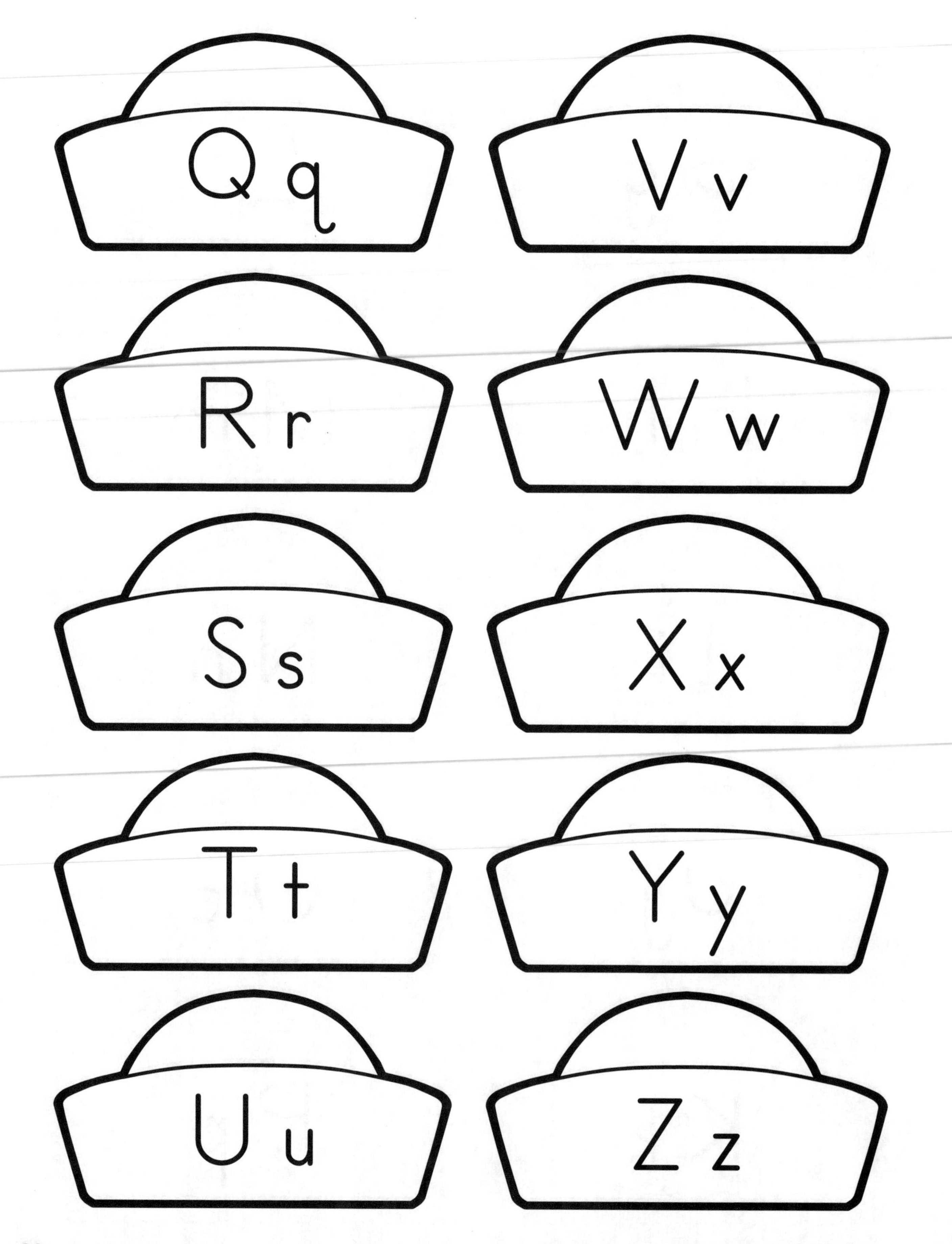

Q q
V v
R r
W w
S s
X x
T t
Y y
U u
Z z

Show and Tell Cards

Show and Tell Cards

Show and Tell Cards

MILK
MILK

Show and Tell Cards